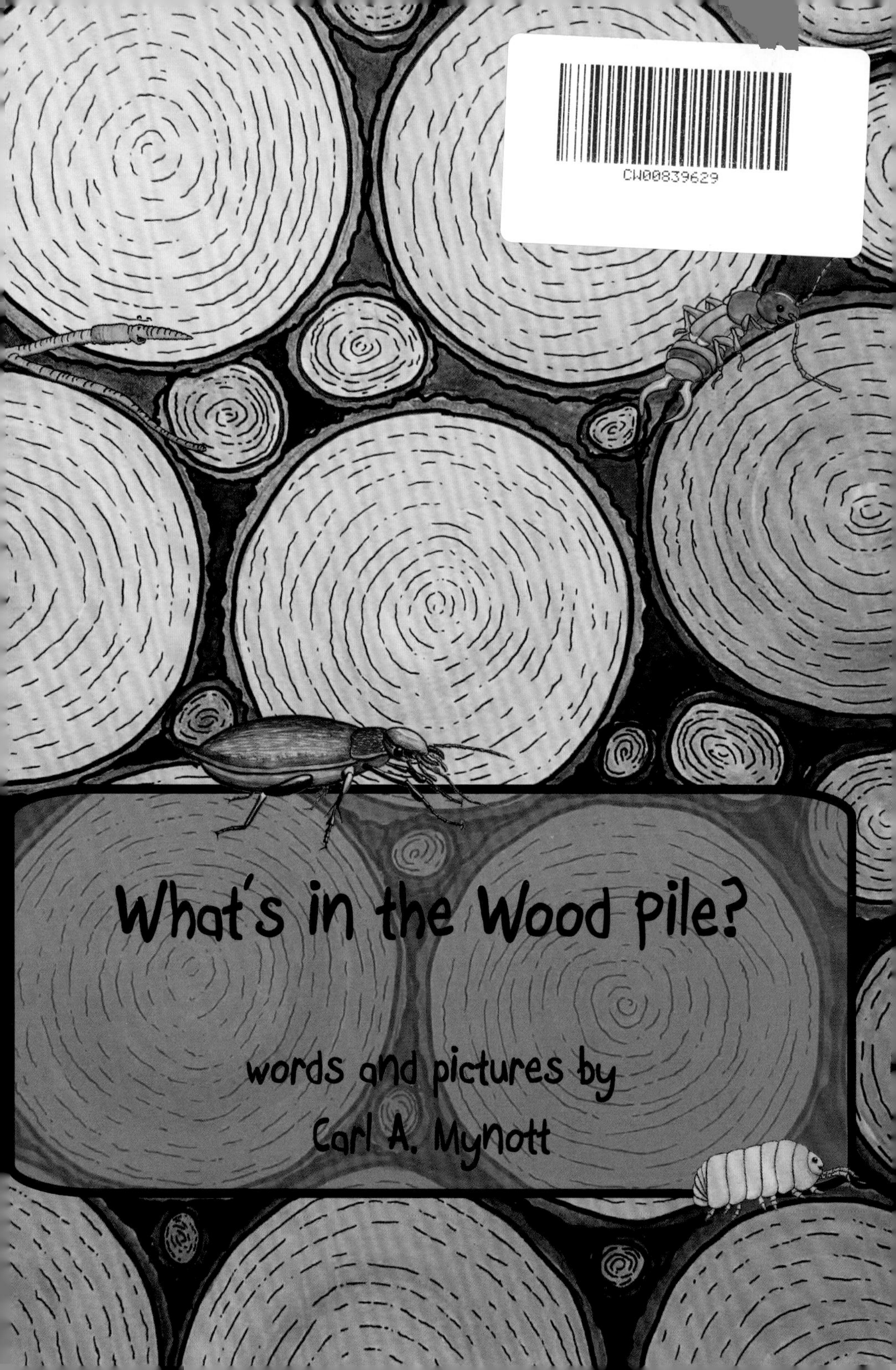
CW00839629
What's in the Wood Pile?
words and pictures by
Carl A. Mynott

What's in the Wood Pile?

First edition published by the author in December 2016.

ISBN 978-0-9929398-3-0

Carl A Mynott
www.britishwildlifetales.co.uk
info@britishwildlifetales.co.uk

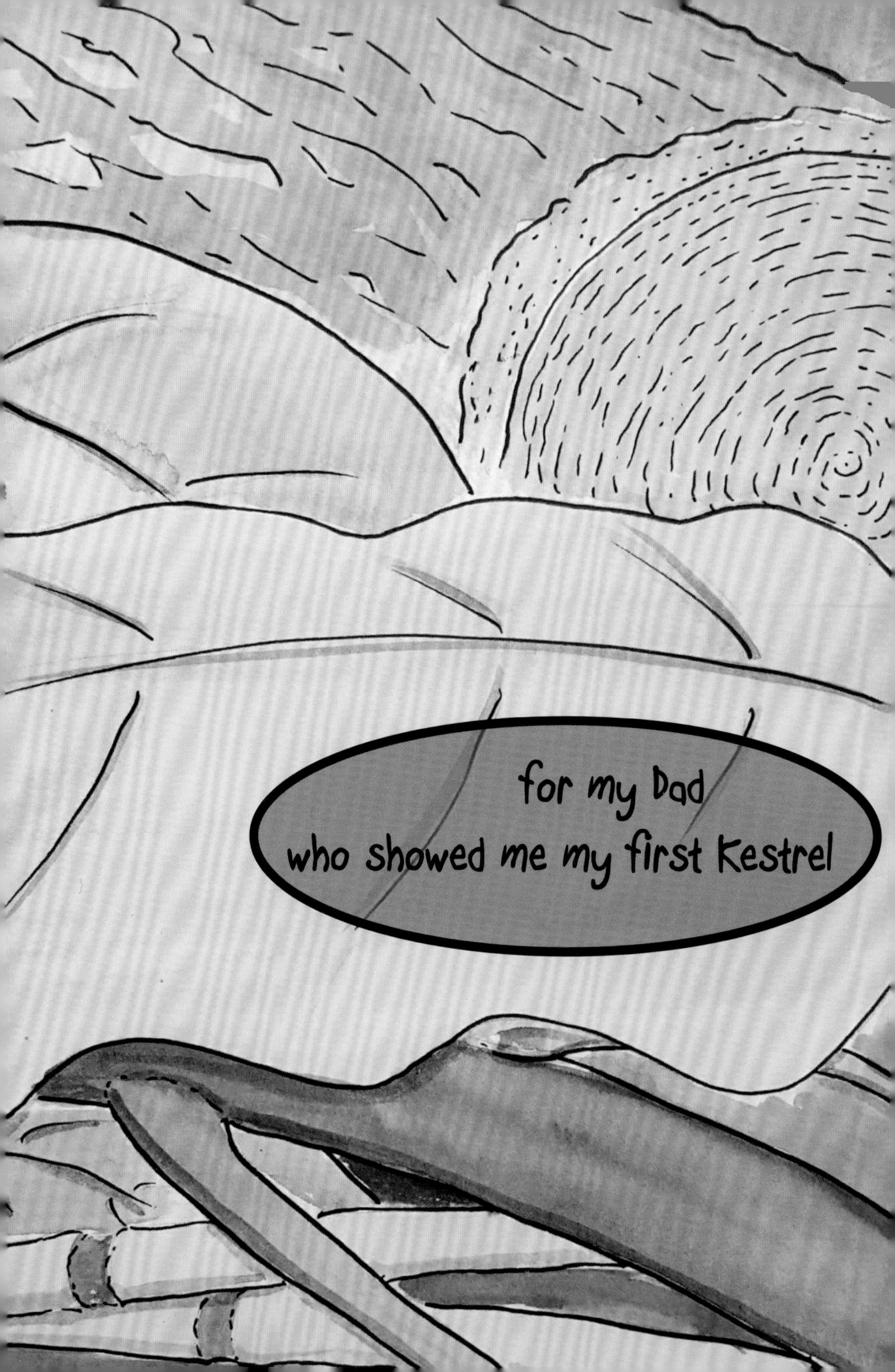
for my Dad
who showed me my first Kestrel

Find the coats and the hats
pull them down from the peg

a wellington boot
for the end of each leg

hurry up Mum
I'll take the lead

let's look round the shed
in the wood and the leaves

Mummy agrees
and replies with a smile

show me then little one
what's in the wood pile?

Lift up the bark
stay as quiet as a mouse

if we're lucky we'll find
a curled up woodlouse

with her shell like a ball
and fourteen grey legs

tucked under her tummy
she keeps twenty four eggs

which she will guard with her life
in her safe hiding patch

for just a few days
until they start to hatch

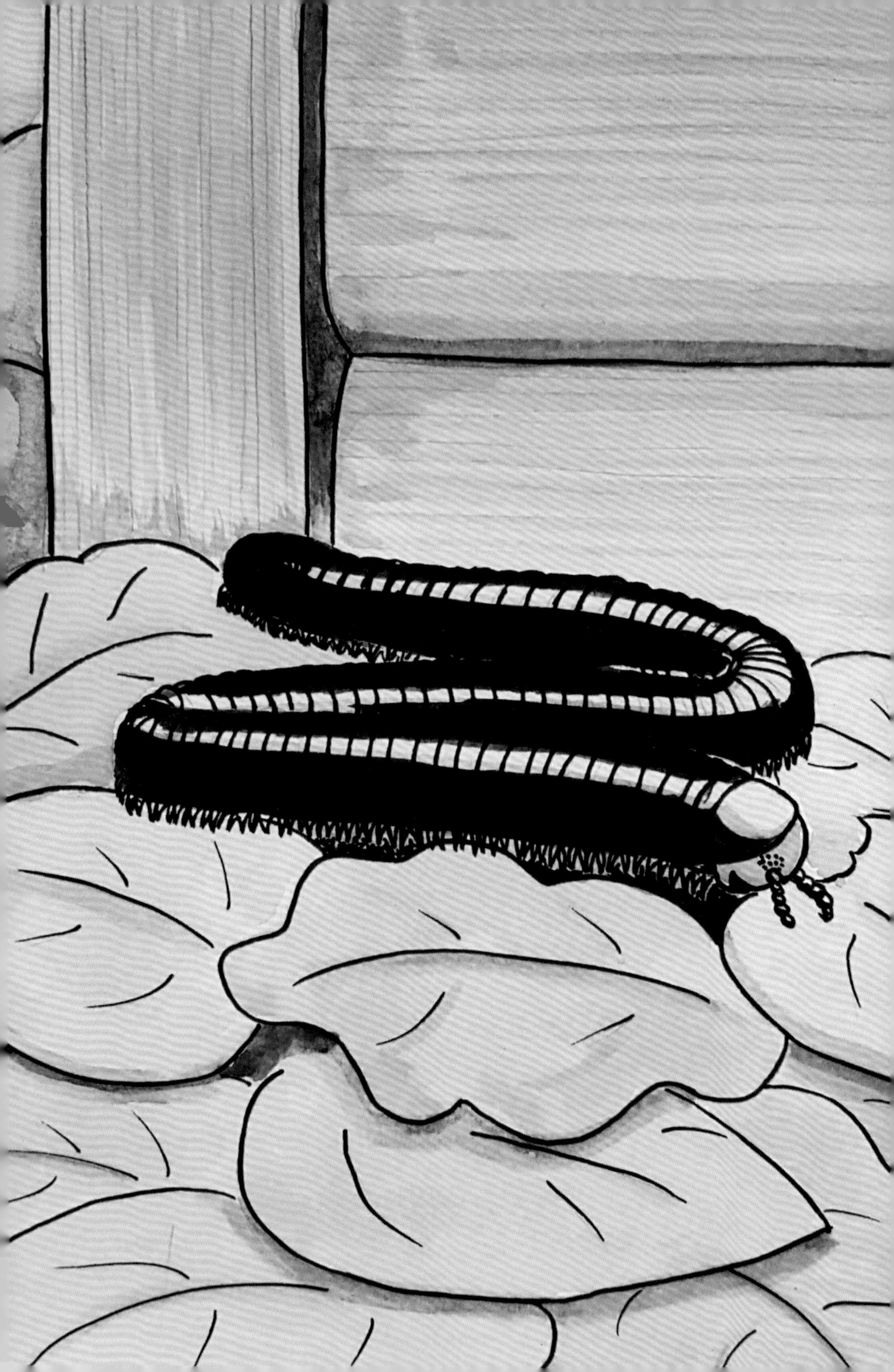

There's a wriggle and a wiggle
at the edge of the bark

a millipede appears
from its home in the dark

with his long and thin body
and shiny black shell

how many legs?
it's so hard to tell

it could be just eighty
or a few hundred more

it moves like a worm
through the leaves on the floor

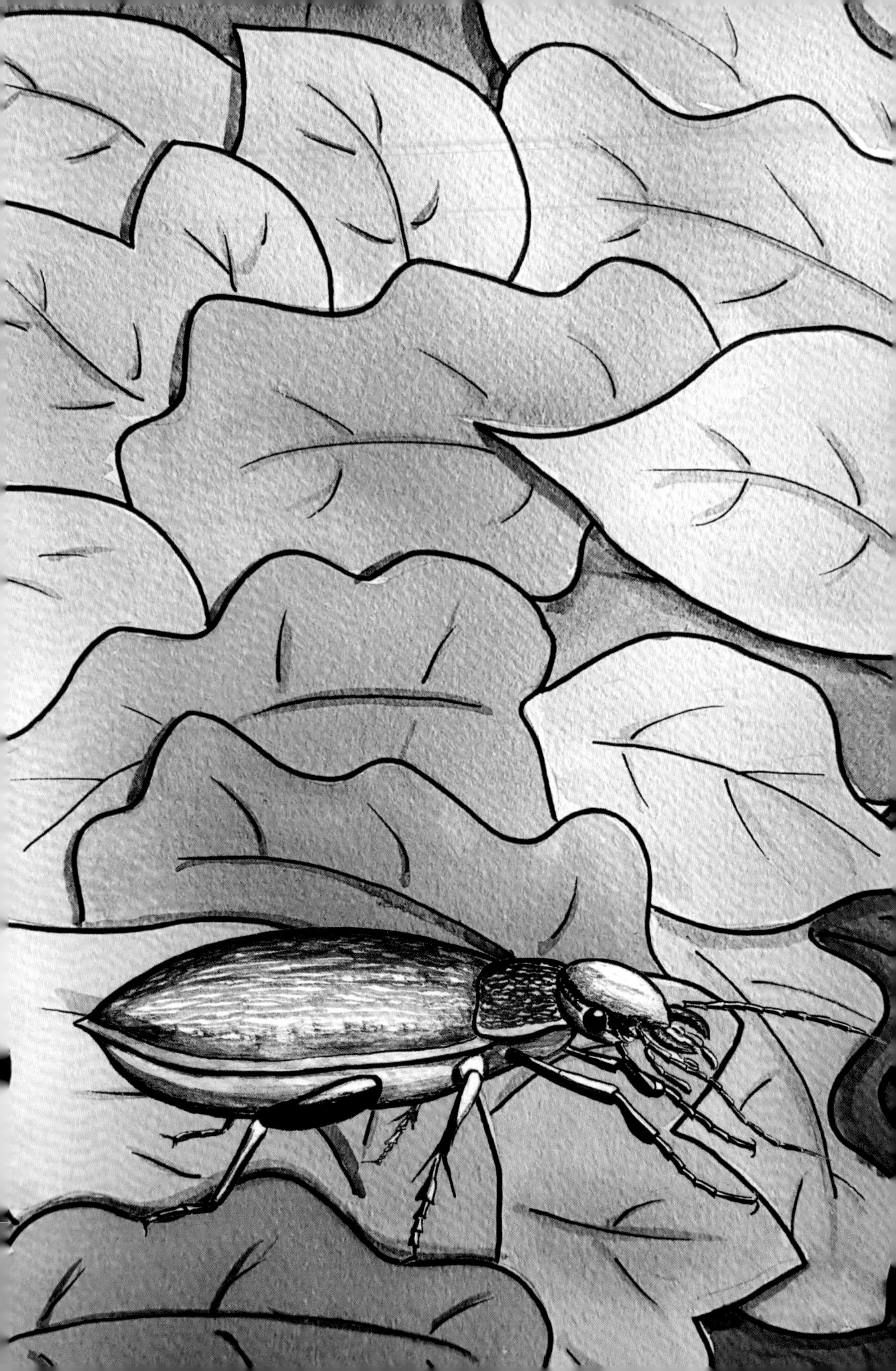

Oh, look! In the corner
a ground beetle zips past

she is all shades of black
and she is ever so fast

she has six long black legs
and two tiny black eyes

the little one gasps
amazed at her size

there's no need to fear
she will cause us no harm

she is tickly good fun
to let crawl up your arm

A tough round brown shell
sits tight on the floor

in the midst of the wood pile
down by the shed door

it's taken all night
to move a few metres

the slimy wet trail
is one of snail's features

little one squints and
wipes the goo from their spectacles

as slowly but surely
emerge four nosey tentacles

Mum lifts a log
and beneath lies a creature

a long, mottled leopard slug
with snail's slimy features

with no tough round shell
it hides under cover

leaving slick silver trails
that cross one another

the slug feeds on leaves
and sometimes Mum's flowers

and moves ever so slowly
their journeys take hours!

There's an old piece of board
by the side of the shed

Mummy says "I know a creature
that uses this as its bed"

under the board
on the moist cool brown soil

a slow worm is snoozing
in a neatly curled coil

it has smooth bronzy skin
and a teeny forked tongue

and each morning warms up
in the heat of the sun

'What is that?!' says Mummy
something catches her eye

"She is a Toad" says the little one
and she is watching those flies

I know she is a Toad
because her skin has those bumps

she walks on her legs
and prefers not to jump

she lays eggs in a pond
once she has mated in spring

a thousand or more
in a long jelly string

Tucked in a fold
in a crispy brown twig

is a beautiful shiny
bronze coloured earwig

he has two strong curved pincers
and a tiny wing case

and six yellow legs
with an ant-like brown face

he is quite safe to hold
but don't let him fall

those pincers are for show
and won't hurt you at all

There is a long thin pink thread
in a groove in the soil

little one reaches out
and the earthworm recoils

they have no eyes, and no ears
no noses or faces

they come out when its wet
to move to new places

they head back underground
to eat stuff that is rotten

like fungus and algae
then make soil with their bottoms

a rustling sound
turns little ones head

as a prickly round animal
shuffles round the shed

it must be quite late because
hedgehog is out

they wait till its dark
to find food with their snouts

it is noisily snuffling
looking for worms

or snails bugs or slugs
well, almost anything that squirms

It's getting quite dark
and an owl stalks a mouse

its time to retreat
to the warmth of the house

heading back to the door
they kick off their boots

Dad is making drinks
while the owl gently hoots

they have had a great day
it has been quite a while

since the last time they looked
for what's in the wood pile.

Help the grown-ups!

What grown ups might miss
you can help them to see

so while you're out in the park
look up to the trees

and down in the grasses
and under the logs

and help them find insects
and shiny green frogs

and ask lots of questions
so they'll want to find out

and they'll start to wonder
what else is about

ow to make your own wood pile...

When they're out in the garden
trimming the hedges

or mowing the lawn
or cutting the edges

gather up the cuttings
the grass and the twigs

start making a pile
it doesn't have to be big

but let it go wild
and quickly you'll see

a wonderful world
where bugs can run free

Which of the creatures of the wood pile have you seen?

Have you seen a Woodlouse?

Have you seen a Millipede?

Have you seen a Ground Beetle?

Have you seen a Snail?

Have you seen a Leopard Slug?

Have you seen a Slow Worm?

Have you seen a Common Toad?

Have you seen an Earwig?

Have you seen an Earthworm?

Have you seen a Hedgehog?

There are many things in life that are important.

Two of them inspired me to begin creating these books.

They are:

My family
and
The natural world

If you do just two things in life, do these:

Love your family

and

Teach them about the natural world.

You're already doing one of them, Thank you for buying my book.

Carl x

BOOKS IN THE BRITISH WILDLIFE TALES SERIES

AVAILABLE NOW

'The Birds at the Bottom of the Garden'

ISBN: 978-0 9929398-0-9

'The Birds Down the Lane'

ISBN: 978-0-9929398-1-6

'What's in the Wood pile?'

(with thanks to Andrew Walker for the title inspiration)

ISBN: 978-0-9929398-3-0

COMING SOON

'What's that Coming Over the Hill?'

featuring 10 amazing creatures that live in our hills and mountains

For more information, and for details about future titles please visit the British Wildlife Tales website at:

www.britishwildlifetales.co.uk